Grade 2

5 Minute Quick Quiz!

Math·Blast
Addition

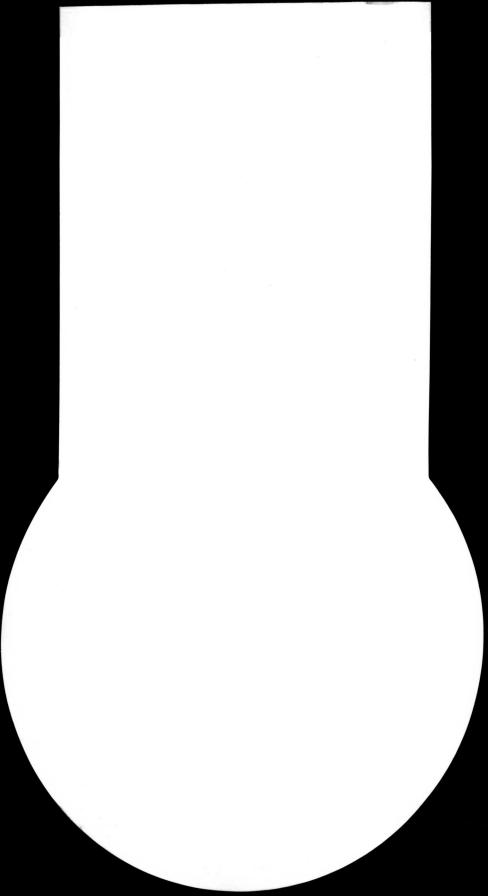

Quick Quiz!

What is missing?

Write the missing numbers.
Check your answers.

Example:

$$\begin{array}{r} 7 \\ + \ 8 \\ \hline \boxed{15} \end{array}$$

The Five Minute Test!

1.
$$\begin{array}{r} 3 \\ + \ 2 \\ \hline \boxed{} \end{array}$$

2.
$$\begin{array}{r} 7 \\ + \ \boxed{} \\ \hline 10 \end{array}$$

3.
$$\begin{array}{r} \boxed{} \\ + \ 4 \\ \hline 12 \end{array}$$

4.
$$\begin{array}{r} \boxed{1} \\ + \ \\ \hline 4 \end{array}$$

5.
$$\begin{array}{r} 9 \\ + \ 3 \\ \hline \boxed{} \end{array}$$

6.
$$\begin{array}{r} 2 \\ + \ \boxed{} \\ \hline 7 \end{array}$$

7.
$$\begin{array}{r} \boxed{} \\ + \ 4 \\ \hline 5 \end{array}$$

8.
$$\begin{array}{r} 5 \\ + \ \boxed{} \\ \hline 10 \end{array}$$

9.
$$\begin{array}{r} 8 \\ + \ 1 \\ \hline \boxed{} \end{array}$$

10.
$$\begin{array}{r} 3 \\ + \ \boxed{} \\ \hline 7 \end{array}$$

11.
$$\begin{array}{r} \boxed{} \\ + \ 2 \\ \hline 3 \end{array}$$

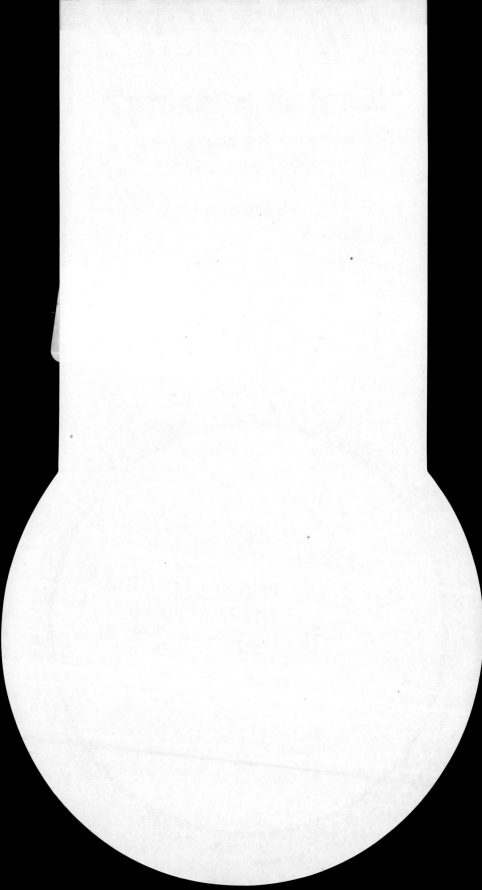

Quick Quiz!

Adding to 20

Complete the problem so each
answer equals 20.

Example:

$$15 + \boxed{5} = 20$$

The Five Minute Test!

1. $2 + \square = 20$

2. $8 + \square = 20$

3. $11 + \square = 20$

4. $6 + \square = 20$

5. $13 + \square = 20$

6. $20 + \square = 20$

7. $4 + \square = 20$

8. $19 + \square = 20$

9. $17 + \square = 20$

Answers: 1. 18, 2. 12, 3. 9, 4. 14, 5. 7, 6. 0, 7. 16, 8. 1, 9. 3

Quick Quiz!

Adding to 30

Complete the problem so each
answer equals 30.

Example:

$20 + \boxed{10} = 30$

The Five Minute Test!

1. $22 + \boxed{} = 30$

2. $18 + \boxed{} = 30$

3. $25 + \boxed{} = 30$

4. $28 + \boxed{} = 30$

5. $4 + \boxed{} = 30$

6. $12 + \boxed{} = 30$

7. $7 + \boxed{} = 30$

8. $19 + \boxed{} = 30$

9. $17 + \boxed{} = 30$

Answers: 1. 8, 2. 12, 3. 5, 4. 2, 5. 26, 6. 18, 7. 23, 8. 11, 9. 13

Quick Quiz!

Plus Plus Plus

Can you solve these long addition problems?

Example:

$5 + 1 + 2 + 3 =$ 11

The Five Minute Test!

1. $9 + 3 + 5 + 2 =$ ☐
2. $8 + 5 + 7 + 4 =$ ☐
3. $6 + 1 + 3 + 2 =$ ☐
4. $1 + 3 + 6 + 5 =$ ☐
5. $3 + 4 + 5 + 1 =$ ☐
6. $2 + 9 + 0 + 5 =$ ☐
7. $8 + 6 + 3 + 4 =$ ☐
8. $9 + 4 + 2 + 5 =$ ☐
9. $2 + 3 + 6 + 4 =$ ☐

Answers: 1. 19, 2. 24, 3. 12, 4. 15, 5. 13, 6. 16, 7. 21, 8. 20, 9. 15

Quick Quiz!

Can you add in your head?

Add and write the sums.

Example:

12 + 13 = ☐ 25

The Five Minute Test!

1. 19 + 11 = ☐
2. 27 + 32 = ☐
3. 43 + 63 = ☐
4. 86 + 25 = ☐
5. 15 + 31 = ☐
6. 30 + 61 = ☐
7. 83 + 94 = ☐
8. 52 + 23 = ☐
9. 66 + 84 = ☐

Answers: 1. 30, 2. 59, 3. 106, 4. 111, 5. 46, 6. 91, 7. 177, 8. 75, 9. 150

Quick Quiz!

Candy Store Stories

Read the stories. Write the answers.

Example:

Danielle bought 12 chocolate bars and 4 pieces of bubble gum. How much candy did Danielle buy?

12
+ 4
_____
 16 pieces of candy

The Five Minute Test!

1. Houston bought 13 lollipops at the candy store. He bought a bag of 100 jelly beans also. How many pieces of candy did he buy?

2. Jazmin bought 35 candy bars and 25 chocolate covered bunny rabbits. How much candy did she buy?

3. Shaye wants to buy 16 gumdrops, 32 pieces of gum, 15 jelly beans, and 2 chocolate bars. She puts the 32 pieces of gum back on the shelf before she pays for her candy. How many pieces of candy does Shaye buy?

Answers: 1. 113 pieces of candy, 2. 60 pieces of candy, 3. 33 pieces of candy

Quick Quiz!

Plus Plus Plus

Can you solve these long
addition problems?

Example:

6 + 2 + 3 + 4 = | 15 |

The Five Minute Test!

1. 8 + 2 + 4 + 1 = ☐
2. 7 + 4 + 6 + 3 = ☐
3. 5 + 0 + 2 + 1 = ☐
4. 0 + 4 + 5 + 4 = ☐
5. 8 + 3 + 4 + 1 = ☐
6. 1 + 8 + 6 + 4 = ☐
7. 9 + 5 + 2 + 8 = ☐
8. 8 + 4 + 1 + 0 = ☐
9. 6 + 5 + 2 + 7 = ☐

Answers: 1. 15, 2. 20, 3. 8, 4. 13, 5. 16, 6. 19, 7. 24, 8. 13, 9. 20

Quick Quiz!

©2012 Dalmatian Press

Can you add in your head?

Add and write the sums.

Example:

35 + 24 = 59

The Five Minute Test!

1. 29 + 13 =

2. 24 + 52 =

3. 93 + 20 =

4. 32 + 41 =

5. 23 + 14 =

6. 48 + 19 =

7. 15 + 30 =

8. 23 + 45 =

9. 16 + 56 =

Quick Quiz!

Baking Stories

Read the stories. Write the answers.

Example:

Joel has 3 eggs, 2 cups of milk, and 1 cup of sugar. How many items does he now have to bake his cake?

$$3 + 2 + 1 = \boxed{6} \text{ items}$$

The Five Minute Test!

1. Megan has 1 cup of flour, 2 eggs, 1 pan, and 26 chocolate chips. How many items does she have to bake her cookies?

2. Steven has 24 graham crackers, 35 marshmallows, 10 chocolate bars, and 10 long sticks. How many items does he have to make his s'mores?

3. Elizabeth has 2 bowls, 1 spoon, 1 pan, 1 bag of sugar, 50 blueberries, and 1 pie crust. How many items does she have to bake her pie?

Answers: 1. 30 items, 2. 79 items, 3. 56 items

Quick Quiz!

Plus Plus Plus

Can you solve these long addition problems?

Example:

$$7 + 3 + 4 + 8 = \boxed{22}$$

The Five Minute Test!

1. $6 + 1 + 8 + 7 = \boxed{}$

2. $9 + 6 + 5 + 2 = \boxed{}$

3. $4 + 7 + 9 + 0 = \boxed{}$

4. $3 + 2 + 7 + 4 = \boxed{}$

5. $2 + 6 + 3 + 8 = \boxed{}$

6. $8 + 1 + 3 + 4 = \boxed{}$

7. $5 + 6 + 7 + 8 = \boxed{}$

8. $0 + 1 + 2 + 3 = \boxed{}$

9. $4 + 5 + 6 + 9 = \boxed{}$

Quick Quiz!

©2012 Dalmatian Press

Can you add in your head?

Add and write the sums.

Example:

40 + 16 = ☐ 56

The Five Minute Test!

1. 10 + 35 = ☐
2. 25 + 78 = ☐
3. 89 + 12 = ☐
4. 42 + 40 = ☐
5. 65 + 22 = ☐
6. 34 + 90 = ☐
7. 45 + 13 = ☐
8. 34 + 77 = ☐
9. 28 + 85 = ☐

Answers: 1. 45, 2. 103, 3. 101, 4. 82, 5. 87, 6. 124, 7. 58, 8. 111, 9. 113

Quick Quiz!

Fruit Stand Stories

Read the stories. Write the answers.

Example:

Ben bought 45 apples, 2 watermelons, and 14 oranges. How many pieces of fruit did he buy?

45 + 2 + 14 = ⬚61⬚ pieces of fruit

The Five Minute Test!

1. Andrew bought 4 strawberries, 12 blueberries, and 23 raspberries. How many berries did he buy?

⬚

2. Emily bought 36 bananas, 23 pears, and 15 kiwi fruits. How many pieces of fruit did she buy?

⬚

3. Brian bought 3 mangoes, 78 cherries, 43 limes, 39 lemons, and 55 apples. How many pieces of fruit did he buy?

⬚

Answers: 1. 39 berries, 2. 74 pieces of fruit, 3. 218 pieces of fruit

Quick Quiz!

Plus Plus Plus

Can you solve these long addition problems?

Example:

$$7 + 8 + 9 + 1 = \boxed{25}$$

The Five Minute Test!

1. $8 + 3 + 4 + 1 =$ ☐
2. $7 + 4 + 5 + 3 =$ ☐
3. $5 + 0 + 2 + 1 =$ ☐
4. $9 + 4 + 5 + 4 =$ ☐
5. $8 + 3 + 5 + 1 =$ ☐
6. $1 + 9 + 6 + 4 =$ ☐
7. $9 + 5 + 3 + 8 =$ ☐
8. $7 + 4 + 1 + 0 =$ ☐
9. $6 + 5 + 4 + 7 =$ ☐

Answers: 1. 16, 2. 19, 3. 8, 4. 22, 5. 17, 6. 20, 7. 25, 8. 12, 9. 22

Quick Quiz!

Challenge adding!

Add and write the sums.

©2012 Dalmatian Press

Example:

235 + 485 = ☐ 720

The Five Minute Test!

1. 219 + 123 = ☐
2. 254 + 562 = ☐
3. 933 + 240 = ☐
4. 352 + 491 = ☐
5. 273 + 104 = ☐
6. 438 + 159 = ☐
7. 195 + 370 = ☐
8. 263 + 485 = ☐
9. 176 + 596 = ☐

Answers: 1. 342, 2. 816, 3. 1173, 4. 843, 5. 377, 6. 597, 7. 565, 8. 748, 9. 772

Quick Quiz!

Toy Stories

Read the stories. Write the answers.

Example:

Emma has a baby doll. She has 3 bottles, 2 blankets, and 3 rattles. How many items does she have for her baby doll?

3 + 2 + 3 = | 8 | doll items

The Five Minute Test!

1. Ayden has 5 trucks, 24 cars, 32 buses, 1 train, 2 airplanes, and 14 boats. How many toy vehicles does he have?

2. Bella likes to play dress-up. She has 4 princess dresses, 26 shoes, 8 fairy wings, 12 magic wands, 37 crowns, 3 hats, 56 gloves, and 4 necklaces. How many dress-up items does she have?

3. Camden likes to build playhouses. He has 13 bed sheets, 15 boxes, 1 roll of tape, 10 chairs, and 1 rope. How many items does he have to build his playhouse?

Answers: 1. 78 toy vehicles, 2. 150 dress-up items, 3. 40 items

Quick Quiz!

©2012 Dalmatian Press

What is missing?

Write the missing numbers.
Check your answers.

Example:

$$\begin{array}{r} \boxed{20} \\ + \ \ 3 \\ \hline 23 \end{array}$$

The Five Minute Test!

1.
$$\begin{array}{r} 23 \\ + \ 12 \\ \hline \Box \end{array}$$

2.
$$\begin{array}{r} 17 \\ + \ \Box \\ \hline 20 \end{array}$$

3.
$$\begin{array}{r} \Box \\ + \ 15 \\ \hline 25 \end{array}$$

4.
$$\begin{array}{r} 11 \\ + \ \Box \\ \hline 25 \end{array}$$

5.
$$\begin{array}{r} 13 \\ + \ 17 \\ \hline \Box \end{array}$$

6.
$$\begin{array}{r} 8 \\ + \ \Box \\ \hline 15 \end{array}$$

7.
$$\begin{array}{r} \Box \\ + 30 \\ \hline 45 \end{array}$$

8.
$$\begin{array}{r} 44 \\ + \ \Box \\ \hline 46 \end{array}$$

9.
$$\begin{array}{r} 22 \\ + \ 14 \\ \hline \Box \end{array}$$

10.
$$\begin{array}{r} 10 \\ + \ \Box \\ \hline 37 \end{array}$$

11.
$$\begin{array}{r} \Box \\ + \ 21 \\ \hline 31 \end{array}$$

Quick Quiz!

©2012 Dalmatian Press

What is missing?

Write the missing numbers.
Check your answers.

Example:

$$\begin{array}{r} 40 \\ + \boxed{35} \\ \hline 75 \end{array}$$

The Five Minute Test!

1. $\begin{array}{r} 50 \\ + 40 \\ \hline \boxed{} \end{array}$

2. $\begin{array}{r} 76 \\ + \boxed{} \\ \hline 90 \end{array}$

3. $\begin{array}{r} \boxed{} \\ + 37 \\ \hline 85 \end{array}$

4. $\begin{array}{r} 34 \\ + \boxed{} \\ \hline 56 \end{array}$

5. $\begin{array}{r} 25 \\ + 88 \\ \hline \boxed{} \end{array}$

6. $\begin{array}{r} 67 \\ + \boxed{} \\ \hline 84 \end{array}$

7. $\begin{array}{r} \boxed{} \\ + 36 \\ \hline 88 \end{array}$

8. $\begin{array}{r} 11 \\ + \boxed{} \\ \hline 66 \end{array}$

9. $\begin{array}{r} 48 \\ + 13 \\ \hline \boxed{} \end{array}$

10. $\begin{array}{r} 15 \\ + \boxed{} \\ \hline 65 \end{array}$

11. $\begin{array}{r} \boxed{} \\ + 56 \\ \hline 99 \end{array}$

Quick Quiz!

Sports Stories

Read the stories. Write the answers.

Example:

Logan plays softball. She has 1 glove, 3 bats, 15 balls, and 1 helmet. How many items does she have for her softball game?

1 + 3 + 15 + 1 = 20 items

The Five Minute Test!

1. Cory plays soccer. He is packing his bag for his game. He packs 1 ball, 2 cleats, 2 chin pads, 1 jersey, 3 bottles of water, and 2 snack bars. How many items does he pack in his bag for his game?

2. Laura is on a tennis team. She is getting ready for a tennis match. She has 1 visor, 1 shirt, 1 skirt, 2 tennis shoes, 6 balls, 1 racket, 5 bottles of water, and 2 armbands. How many items does she have for her tennis match?

3. Patrick is at basketball practice. He has 4 teammates. They all have a ball of their own. How many total basketballs are there?

Answers: 1. 11 items, 2. 19 items, 3. 5 basketballs

Quick Quiz!

What is missing?

Write the missing numbers.
Check your answers.

Example:

$$\begin{array}{r} 78 \\ + \ 11 \\ \hline \boxed{89} \end{array}$$

The Five Minute Test!

1. $\begin{array}{r} 33 \\ + \ 22 \\ \hline \square \end{array}$

2. $\begin{array}{r} 14 \\ + \ \square \\ \hline 30 \end{array}$

3. $\begin{array}{r} \square \\ + \ 23 \\ \hline 44 \end{array}$

4. $\begin{array}{r} 62 \\ + \ \square \\ \hline 80 \end{array}$

5. $\begin{array}{r} 55 \\ + \ 11 \\ \hline \square \end{array}$

6. $\begin{array}{r} 12 \\ + \ \square \\ \hline 25 \end{array}$

7. $\begin{array}{r} \square \\ + \ 45 \\ \hline 93 \end{array}$

8. $\begin{array}{r} 19 \\ + \ \square \\ \hline 64 \end{array}$

9. $\begin{array}{r} 10 \\ + \ 29 \\ \hline \square \end{array}$

10. $\begin{array}{r} 16 \\ + \ \square \\ \hline 37 \end{array}$

11. $\begin{array}{r} \square \\ + \ 16 \\ \hline 72 \end{array}$

Quick Quiz!

It gets harder...

Write the missing numbers.
Check your answers.

Example:

$$\begin{array}{r} 100 \\ + \boxed{324} \\ \hline 424 \end{array}$$

The Five Minute Test!

1.
$$\begin{array}{r} 333 \\ + 423 \\ \hline \boxed{} \end{array}$$

2.
$$\begin{array}{r} 300 \\ + \boxed{} \\ \hline 567 \end{array}$$

3.
$$\begin{array}{r} \boxed{} \\ + 145 \\ \hline 789 \end{array}$$

4.
$$\begin{array}{r} 890 \\ + 100 \\ \hline \boxed{} \end{array}$$

5.
$$\begin{array}{r} 167 \\ + \boxed{} \\ \hline 689 \end{array}$$

6.
$$\begin{array}{r} \boxed{} \\ + 134 \\ \hline 437 \end{array}$$

7.
$$\begin{array}{r} 607 \\ + 255 \\ \hline \boxed{} \end{array}$$

8.
$$\begin{array}{r} 567 \\ + \boxed{} \\ \hline 781 \end{array}$$

9.
$$\begin{array}{r} \boxed{} \\ + 453 \\ \hline 546 \end{array}$$

Quick Quiz!

©2012 Dalmatian Press

Up to a challenge?

Write the missing numbers.
Check your answers.

Example:

$$\boxed{478}$$
$$+\ 115$$
$$\overline{593}$$

The Five Minute Test!

1.
$$142$$
$$+\ 351$$
$$\overline{\boxed{}}$$

2.
$$401$$
$$+\ \boxed{}$$
$$\overline{689}$$

3.
$$\boxed{}$$
$$+\ 234$$
$$\overline{886}$$

4.
$$792$$
$$+\ 167$$
$$\overline{\boxed{}}$$

5.
$$122$$
$$+\ \boxed{}$$
$$\overline{439}$$

6.
$$\boxed{}$$
$$+\ 287$$
$$\overline{641}$$

7.
$$763$$
$$+\ 222$$
$$\overline{\boxed{}}$$

8.
$$356$$
$$+\ \boxed{}$$
$$\overline{532}$$

9.
$$\boxed{}$$
$$+\ 252$$
$$\overline{746}$$

Quick Quiz!

Up and add 'em!

Write the missing numbers.
Check your answers.

©2012 Dalmatian Press

Example:

$$
\begin{array}{r}
589 \\
+\ 342 \\
\hline
\boxed{931}
\end{array}
$$

The Five Minute Test!

1.
$$
\begin{array}{r}
703 \\
+\ 125 \\
\hline

\end{array}
$$

2.
$$
\begin{array}{r}
678 \\
+\ \\
\hline
831
\end{array}
$$

3.
$$
\begin{array}{r}
 \\
+\ 145 \\
\hline
785
\end{array}
$$

4.
$$
\begin{array}{r}
879 \\
+\ 134 \\
\hline

\end{array}
$$

5.
$$
\begin{array}{r}
586 \\
+\ \\
\hline
833
\end{array}
$$

6.
$$
\begin{array}{r}
 \\
+\ 600 \\
\hline
913
\end{array}
$$

7.
$$
\begin{array}{r}
123 \\
+\ 765 \\
\hline

\end{array}
$$

8.
$$
\begin{array}{r}
863 \\
+\ \\
\hline
999
\end{array}
$$

9.
$$
\begin{array}{r}
 \\
+\ 233 \\
\hline
713
\end{array}
$$

Answers: 1. 828, 2. 153, 3. 640, 4. 1013, 5. 247, 6. 313, 7. 888, 8. 136, 9. 480

Quick Quiz!

The Ultimate Challenge

Example :

$$200 + 147 = \boxed{347}$$

The Five Minute Test!

1. 1000 + 200 + 5 =

2. Is 38 more or less than 25 + 12?

3. What is 43 + 18 + 27?

4. What is 1 + 2 + 3 + 4 + 5 + 6 + 7 + 8?

5. Is 16 more or less than 3 + 14?

6. How many more than 112 is 137?

7. How many more than 382 is 420?

8. Add 456 + 789.

Answers: 1. 1205, 2. more, 3. 88, 4. 36, 5. less, 6. 25, 7. 38, 8. 1245

Quick Quiz!

The Ultimate Challenge

©2012 Dalmatian Press

Example:

How many more than 14 is 23? `9`

The Five Minute Test!

1. Is 14 more or less than 12 + 1? ☐

2. How many more than 65 is 86? ☐

3. What is 8 + 9 + 7 + 6 + 4 + 5 + 3? ☐

4. How many more than 62 is 95? ☐

5. Is 95 + 32 more or less than 110 + 14? ☐

6. What is 48 + 78 + 67 + 94 + 63? ☐

7. How many more than 857 is 976? ☐

8. Is 44 + 45 more or less than 15 + 76? ☐

Answers: 1. more, 2. 21, 3. 42, 4. 33, 5. more 6. 350, 7. 119, 8. less